Kama Sutra

Knowledge for Men

Knowledge for Men

*

Text:
Manjushri Basu

*

Lustre Press
Roli Books

ISBN: 978-81-7436-174-5

Text:
Manjusri Basu

Photographs:
Roli Books Collection,
Victoria & Albert Museum, Lance Dane

© **Roli & Janssen BV 2010**
Published in India by
Roli Books in arrangement
with Roli & Janssen
M-75, Greater Kailash-II Market
New Delhi-110 048, India.
Phone: ++91-11-4068 2000
Fax: ++91-11-2921 7185
Email: info@rolibooks.com
Website: www.rolibooks.com

Printed and bound in India

Contents

*Man, the eternal hunter in the game of love, has been
seeking the object of his affection down the ages.
But the chase is not yet over.*

Introduction

It has stretched the minds of poets, philosophers, pirates, priests, politicians, thinkers, doers, kings and queens, you and I. It has made men mad, made them ecstatic, made them divine.

What is this thing called love? Is it physics, chemistry, biology? Is it a science? Or an art? Poetry, music, painting, theatre? Or metaphysics, perhaps?

Maybe in another millennium or two we may have some answers.

In fact, almost 2000 years ago, one wise man set out on a similar quest. The Indian sage, Vatsyayana, devoted the better part of his time and life to some serious research on the interaction between men and women. The result was one of the best-known books in the world – the *Kama Sutra* – a treatise on love.

The *Kama Sutra* means different things to different people. To some it stands for the Erotic East, to others it is a salacious piece of writing, sanctified merely by its antiquity. To others still, it is a scholarly thesis, amazing in its breadth and depth. There are also those who find it in turns boring and hilarious, old-fashioned, pedantic and sexist. It is all of this – and more.

We look at the *Kama Sutra* from yet another angle. It is timeless and universal in the concepts that it sets out. It is frank, candid and completely free of any guilt while discussing sex. Yes, the language of the original is archaic. But Vatsyayana wrote his book as a serious text in formal Sanskrit, not for popular tastes. And the original translators remained faithful to the spirit and letter of the treatise.

The appeal of the *Kama Sutra* lies in this: that when you take away the idiom, the substance does not suffer. That no matter how you twist and turn the language, no matter in what mould you choose to cast your words, the basic facts still ring true.

It is in this spirit that we present this elegant twin-set of volumes. A his-and-hers version, which is based entirely on the precepts that sage Vatsyayana set out in the *Kama Sutra*.

What you will find in this volume is the man's point of view. Yet it relates entirely to the woman. Read it by yourself and read it with her. It gives you the freedom to do both – enjoy your privacy and savour your togetherness.

∾

The Kama Sutra enjoins a guilt-free sexual life where pleasures are to be freely but gracefully tasted.

A Man and His World

$\mathcal{E}$ach stage in a man's life has its own purpose. Childhood is for learning from books, teachers, games. Youth is for experimenting and for learning of a different sort – from one's mistakes. Maturity is for leading a full, satisfying life as a good citizen and a discerning adult.

Vatsyayana recommends that once you are done with studies, you should look at settling down to the life of a householder. Collect your wealth and resources coming from inheritance, gifts, war, trade or business and buy yourself a house in a respectable neighbourhood, or at least, close to where other like-minded men and women dwell.

Ideally your home should be near a lake or river and have different rooms for different activities: preferably, a set of public rooms and another set of private areas. Make sure there's some open space for fresh air and some form of a garden or greenery.

Decorate your living room creatively with objects that please the senses. Fresh flowers, good

~

Your home mirrors your world. Make it spacious, green, have different areas for public and private activities.

*Even in those ancient times, Vatsyayana was
recommending a beauty treatment for men –
it's not just a modern fad.*

paintings, soft carpets, attractive fruits and other
edibles, fragrances and air fresheners. Don't forget
to include good books, good music – even musical
instruments if you happen to play any. And, of
course, section off a small area of your home as a
craft or hobby centre.

Your bed should be large, comfortable and
always clean, neat and attractive to the eye. An

artistic canopy is desirable, as also two pillows, one at the head and the other at the foot.

Now Vatsyayana's attention turns to you. He says that physical cleanliness is an absolute must. After your ablutions first thing in the morning, you need to clean your teeth, splash a judicious amount of perfume on yourself, darken your eyes with kohl, redden your lips with the juice of *paan* or betel and sweeten your breath. Don't think he stops there – he's nothing if not thorough! You should bathe daily, massage yourself with fragrant oils every two days, use soap and shampoo every third day and shave every fourth day. You should depilate body hair regularly and scrape off the sweat from your armpits. A tough beauty routine to follow, but think of the rewards!

As for food, three meals a day is the recommendation. After breakfast, spend some time teaching your exotic pet birds like parrots and mynahs to talk. Follow that up by watching cock, quail and ram fights. Before your midday nap spend some time with learned men, skilled conversationalists and those with a great sense of humour to deepen your own wisdom and hone your wit.

Dress up for the evening in all your fine feathers including jewellery. Light the lamp and the incense at home and wait for your beloved to come. You may also send someone to fetch her or go and get her yourself. Welcome her in with all courtesy and entertain her well with lively conversation, attractively prepared food and pleasant diversions. These should be your activities on ordinary days.

On special occasions and festival days, it's your duty to help organise celebrations to honour your deities. Always be quick and generous in your contributions of time and money for religious and community causes. Be especially courteous to those who have come from afar for these festivities.

As for intellectual gatherings, make sure you hold them regularly either in your house or at a friend's place where good humour, literary repartee and wit flow. When it's your turn to throw a party, never ever cut corners. Have the best of everything – décor, food, drink and, of course, great company! Go out often for picnics and other outdoor entertainment. Choose shady glens with

~

Seize the day and enjoy being a man, focusing your attention on women and gaining their affection.

*Clean, neat and large, with two pillows and an artistic
canopy – that's how Vatsyayana likes your bed,
a vital accessory.*

flowing water or a lake nearby. Take along good
food and drink, leave at dawn, gambol in the water
all day with women and at dusk wend your way
homeward. How delicious it is to be tired then!

And your friends, how should you choose
them? The best, according to Vatsyayana, are
childhood friends, followed by those bound by
obligation, those who are like-minded, your fellow
students, those who know your secrets and faults
as you know theirs, your nurse's child, one who
was brought up with you and those whose families

*Mark your passion with a fine aesthetic sense, always be
courteous and never descend to vulgarity.*

share friendships with yours. Give your friends what
you expect from them in return – sincerity, loyalty,
companionship and help in hard times. Give trust in
return for trust and never insult them. Remember,
courtesy is the gentleman's hallmark.

Similarly, your choice of a sexual companion
should always be bound by the ethics of the society
you live in. In Vatsyayana's time, there were four
broad categories of women who could be freely
enjoyed by men: 1. Young, unattached women who
were not promiscuous; 2. Women twice-married
without having been widowed; 3. Public women;

and 4. Women resorted to for some special purpose other than pleasure or progeny. (This last group seems to be different, in the sense that men resort to them not out of love or lust but use them as a means to gain something.) Today, those groupings sound incorrect if not downright weird, but the message remains the same: choose with care and concern for yourself and your lover and for the world around you.

As for the ways in which you woo her, win her and keep her, remember one simple rule: read the book but trust your instincts.

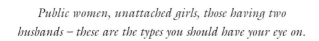

Public women, unattached girls, those having two husbands – these are the types you should have your eye on.

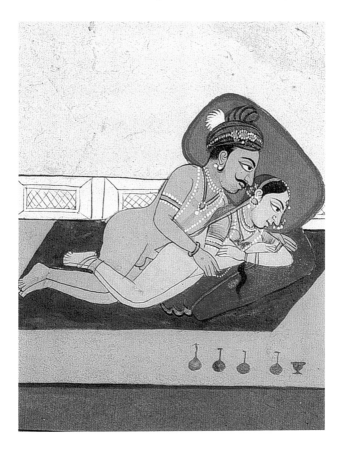

Understanding Her

*T*hat phrase, 'understanding her', is so much easier to say than follow. Woman is not a scientific formula with a definite set of givens from which only one truth can emerge. The human mind is not bound by any set of rules – especially not by the ones we make ourselves!

But Vatsyayana seems to have had a shrewd understanding of the way our minds and bodies work. The previous chapter listed his broad categories of women that could be chosen as lovers. Elaborating, he classifies types of women who are easily seduced and others who aren't.

And who are these women more than willing to fall into your arms, not to mention your bed? The *Kama Sutra* lists them as: those who stand in the doorways of houses and peer out into the street; those who constantly gossip in their neighbours' houses; those who always stare at men; a female messenger; one who constantly steals glances at men; she whose husband has without cause

~

Judge a woman by her conduct, counsels the sage; let patience, perseverance and strategy be your watchwords if you decide to woo her.

taken up with another woman; one who loathes
her husband; one who has no children; one of
indefinite caste; one whose children are dead; one
married to a man who is inferior to her; one who
has grown up to abhor her husband, a rich man

～

*If she agrees to meet you in private or is dressed
especially for you, she will be yours easily.*

to whom she was married off when a child; one who is looking for a man of wisdom to match her own; one who does not get the respect she deserves; one whose husband is given to constant travelling; one who is jealous, covetous, immoral or barren. In other words, those who are extroverts, uninhibited, unattached, looking for greener pastures or iconoclasts are easy to win over.

But stay away from the wives of other men, especially if the men are your friends, relatives, superiors, priests or rulers. In general, wives are taboo unless they are being used as a means to some end, for instance, revenge or gain.

Some other women are to be avoided as well: those with infectious diseases, lunatics, outcasts; those who cannot keep secrets, wantons; those who are unnaturally white or unnaturally black; foul-smelling women; those who are near-relations, friends or ascetics. Some of us may find these labels hopelessly outdated and even insensitive. But which of us has not come across at least some of the kinds of women Vatsyayana listed 15 centuries ago?

How do you know when Ms Right comes by? Some sages tell us you can know a woman's character, will and passion from her physical marks and signs, that is, by physique. But Vatsyayana feels women should be judged by their conduct, by the outward expressions of their thoughts and by their body language – by their psyche, as it were.

Thus, when you pursue a woman, try to read her mind and then act. If she hears you out but doesn't say what she wants, you should use the services of a trusted go-between. If she meets you once and repeats the encounter in better dress, or agrees to

*These are her love signs: she delights in your company and
prolongs it, is tongue-tied, steals glances from afar, always
puts on what you have gifted her.*

meet in private, surely she will be yours with little
persuasion. A woman who leads you on a long
chase is a trifler. But owing to the fickleness of

the human mind, even *she* can be conquered – persevere. When a woman avoids your overtures it is difficult to win her, but keep in constant touch and take the help of a clever mediator. One who rejects you with harsh words needs patient wooing. All that Vatsyayana's trying to say is that patience, perseverance and strategy win in the end.

When a woman falls in love, she always shows her true feelings through words and actions. You need to interpret them right. When she's in love she never looks directly at you and becomes bashful at your gaze. She steals glances from afar. She becomes tongue-tied when you speak to her. She delights in your company for long periods. She speaks to her companions in a particular tone to draw your attention when you move away. Finds inconsequential things to show to you or narrates stories very slowly so that she can keep you by her side. Kisses and embraces any child when you happen to be around. Is graceful and coy when her friends tease her in front of you. Confides in your friends and tries to win them over. Is kind to your servants and delights in hearing their stories about you. Avoids being seen by you when she's not elegantly turned out. Gifts you an ornament or bauble that you had asked to see. Always wears what you have gifted her. Becomes dejected when her parents mention any other suitor.

Do you see any of this in the one you love? Go all out to woo and win her then. Vatsyayana says a young girl should be won over by childlike sports, a damsel come of age by your skill in the arts and a girl that loves you through her confidantes.

The Art of Seduction

There is finesse, there is subtlety, there is wit in the art of seduction. But above all, there is a science. Or call it strategy if you will: definite steps that will lead you to your goal.

Vatsyayana says the direct approach works best unless circumstances are totally against it. And no, he doesn't mean the caveman-and-club scene! Women love men who do their own wooing, but they absolutely adore those who do it in style.

First of all, you need to be seen by her in a desirable and controlled setting – at a friend's place, at the home of a respectable person, on a social occasion or during festivities. This guarantees you will be on your best behaviour! Then, you need to attract her attention, but subtly. Look at her so as to make your intentions plain. Tug at a moustache, make a noise with your nails, play with your jewellery or tinkle your ornaments. When she looks at you, talk about her to those around you, show her you enjoy the finer things of life. When you are sitting next to a woman friend, feign indifference.

~

The best approach is the direct one but make sure you do it in style and, especially, in a controlled setting.

Don't be hasty for sex. The path to intimacy is long,
sinuously filled with endearments, and keeps twisting and
turning with the games of love.

Carry on a conversation of double entendres with any person, so that she can pick up your meaning.

The presence of a child is important in Vatsyayana's scheme of seduction. He recommends that you play with the child if one happens to be sitting on her lap, pretend to give it something and then take it back – in other words, show your tender and playful nature. That's how you can endear yourself. Make yourself agreeable to her relatives too, so that you can start visiting her at home. In her house you could begin your campaign by talking of love within her hearing, but not in her presence.

Sometimes, the oblique approach works better. It works especially well with young girls. You should approach them with delicacy and caution. Give lavishly (of course within your means) of gifts. Do make sure that whatever you give – be it clothes, objets d'art, jewellery or even flowers – is of the best quality that you can afford. That shows your high regard. At a party ask her to give you her corsage or the flower tucked in her hair.

And now, you can move on to physical intimacy. Make it a point to touch her 'accidentally'. Brush a hand against a hip, a shoulder or a breast. Find an excuse to move up close. (Of course, if Vatsyayana had been born in the western world he would have been sure to include dancing as one of the forms of socially acceptable erotic behaviour. As it is, his other advice more than makes up for this lack.)

If you happen to be swimming together, he says you should dive far away from her and then suddenly surface very close to her. Many of us have used this technique with great success, not

Stay faithful to one woman, pour out your love in deeds and
words and never make the mistake of seducing two women
at one time.

to mention grabbing her leg or tickling her feet underwater. At other times, sit close to her, place your foot on hers and slowly press her toes one by one. If she likes it, repeat the action with her foot in your hand now. Whenever you have the chance to touch her (as when handing her something or taking something from her), let it be a slow, lingering touch, full of the love you feel for her. Kiss her gently and when she doesn't object too much, let your desire build up to more explicit caresses.

But no woman is won by deeds alone. Despite protests and seeming exasperation, every woman loves to be wooed with words. Therefore put your heart on your tongue, coat it with honey and offer it to her. Speak to her of your great love and how you cannot bear to be without her. Pretend to be ill and insist that only her touch will make you well again. Take her on a stroll and admire the beauties of nature, but make sure you don't admire them more than her face and form!

At last, this amazing game of seduction draws to its climax when both of you are ready to enjoy sex.

Vatsyayana has a gentle word of warning for ardent men. You should never try to seduce two women at the same time. Both of them will be able to see through your lack of sincerity and you'll end up winning neither. Make sure you've won over one of them and secure her affections before moving on to another. Again, if you value your reputation (as all wise men should) you should not pursue a woman who is timid, scared, untrustworthy, well-guarded or has a father-in-law or mother-in-law in the vicinity.

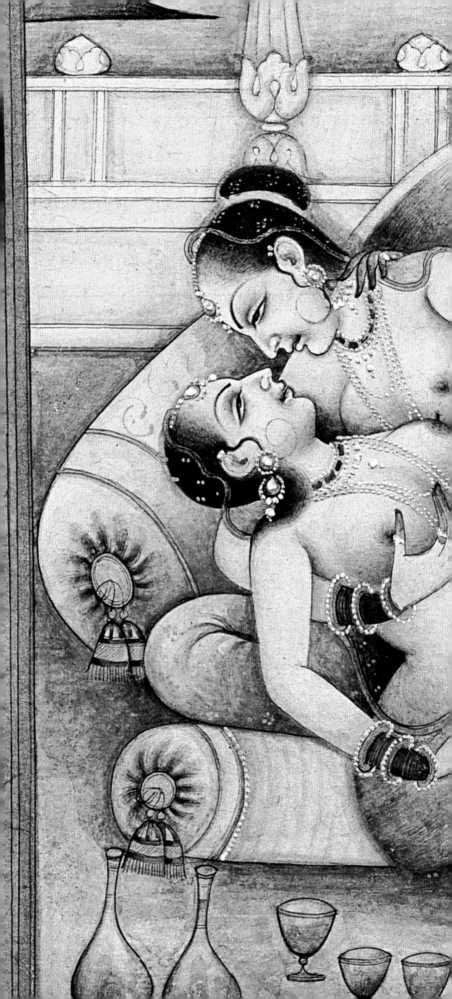

How Do I Love Her?

Most of the world is familiar with the *Kama Sutra's* famous classifications. The lists go by threes. There are three types of men according to the sizes of their penises – rabbit (small), bull (medium) and horse (large). Similarly, among women, depending on the depths of their vaginas, there are the deer (small), the mare (medium) and the elephant (large). It is important to note here that size has nothing to do with intensity of passion or performance.

Among both men and women there are three degrees of desire – low, middling and intense. As for duration, again there are three divisions for both men and women – short, medium and prolonged.

Work out all the combinations and we have 729 possible unions, a mind-boggling figure. However, Vatsyayana says that like with like is the best possible union in all cases. For instance: a rabbit man goes best with a deer woman, a man of low passion hits it off with a woman of a similar nature and a man

Vatsyayana's triads of sex are: three types of women, three degrees of desire and three durations of pleasure.

who performs for a short duration is best suited to a woman who performs the same way. This rule applies similarly to the other categories as well. But with skill and passion any combination is possible and pleasurable.

There is a long discourse on the nature of a man's passion and how it differs from a woman's. Ultimately, Vatsyayana concludes a man's role is active while a woman's is passive but both derive equal pleasure and show it physically – the man by ejaculating, the woman by having an orgasm.

~

Meet your lady love with sense and style: dress with care, behave with courtesy, be attentive to her friends, and seduce with disarming guile and charm.

He also mentions that by reason of her physical and mental make-up the woman takes longer for arousal and foreplay is essential to her pleasure.

Is it possible to classify embraces? Apparently yes, since Vatsyayana does so in great detail, including some we wouldn't see as falling in that category.

At the most basic level there are four kind of embraces: touching, piercing, rubbing and pressing.

❋ Try and get close to her on some pretext and brush your body lightly against hers. She may do the same to you. This is the 'touching' embrace.

❋ Sometimes a woman comes close to you and on the pretext of reaching out for something touches you with her breasts. This is the 'piercing'

embrace. It's quite the done thing to give her breasts a slight pressure as an acknowledgement. These two embraces usually happen between those who are not very well acquainted. Rubbing and pressing are usually done between lovers:

✳ The two of you walk very close to each other and let your bodies rub against each other.

✳ One of you presses the other hard up against a wall with the whole body.

As experienced lovers you can practice the following very beautiful embraces which have equally evocative names. The first two are done standing up, the next two while lying down in bed.

✳ She twines her limbs around you, pulls your head down to meet her willing lips and looks at you adoringly. This is called the 'twining of the creeper'.

~

If desire finds you both trying to merge into one regardless of pain, you are enjoying 'the mixing of milk and water'.

✳ When she places one foot on yours and twines the other leg around your thigh, puts one arm behind your back and the other around your shoulder and tries to kiss you while uttering soft cries of joy, she's 'climbing the tree'.

✳ Lie down facing each other and really close so that your arms, thighs and torsos are pressed together tightly and rubbing against each other. This is called the 'mixing of sesame seed and rice'.

✳ Both of you are so inflamed that you grasp and entwine each other tightly as if to merge your bodies into one regardless of pain. She could be either sitting in your lap or facing you in bed. This embrace is termed the 'mixing of milk and water'.

During sex, there are another four embraces to enhance your experience. All of these can be done either sitting up or lying down:

✳ Either or both of you press the muscular part of one of your partner's thighs between your own. This is the 'thigh embrace'.

✳ She lifts a thigh to press on her pelvis, inviting you to enter her while you urge up her hips to meet your own in the close 'pelvic embrace'.

✳ She presses her breasts firmly on to your chest in the 'breast embrace'.

✳ When either of you touches the other's forehead, eyes or mouth repeatedly and intensely with your own it's called the 'forehead embrace'.

And now to kisses and other marks of increased passion. Come to think of it, kisses, love bites and nail marks are really forms of embraces. They are limited to specific parts of the body and are more intense, while embraces are all encompassing.

Kissing is done solely by the lips, teeth and tongue. Vatsyayana describes many types of kisses such as the 'touching' kiss, the 'throbbing' kiss and the 'greatly pressed' kiss. There are also embraces like 'the kiss of the upper lip', the 'slanted' kiss and the 'upturned' kiss.

Believe it or not, there's a where, how and when to kissing too! He says there are specific areas to be kissed to enhance arousal – the forehead, eyes, cheeks, throat, bosom, breasts (including nipples), lips and the inside of the mouth. But he also says that once passion takes over there's no limit to the places on your lover's body that you will want to kiss!

There are four kinds of kisses: light, moderate, firm and forceful. Light, gentle kisses are for the forehead and eyes; moderate kisses may be given on the breasts, nipples, arms and earlobes; firm kisses are for the chest, groin, sides; and forceful kisses are mainly on the mouth, cheeks, navel and bosom. According to the sage, kisses can take place at any time, but most intensely just before sexual union.

When you come home late at night and she's sleeping, you should try giving her a kiss to rouse her and arouse her as well. Passionate lovers are known to kiss their beloved's reflection in the mirror or her picture when she's not there. Kissing her fingers is usually done in company or at night when it can become an incredibly erotic experience. Returning embrace for embrace, kiss for kiss is how you stoke your mutual passion.

Nail and teeth marks form an important part of Vatsyayana's instructions. They are made on special occasions – before going on a journey or after returning from one, on making up after a quarrel, or when she is high after a party – and they are for people of great passion. It is the man who makes the marks to show his love and esteem. Today we'd perhaps interpret it as a 'hands off' warning to others! Places for nail marks are the upper arms, the bosom, neck, back, waist, buttocks and thighs. Then there are types of marks: gentle (when you run your nail down her arm or her belly to give her goose pimples), crescent-shaped, circular, in lines, like a tiger's claw or even like a peacock's foot. Barring the first, all leave a lasting impression. What Vatsyayana calls teeth marks we call love bites. He says love bites can be given in all the places fit for kissing except the upper lip, the eyes and the tongue. Those who have uneven, protruding, loosely set teeth should not attempt to bestow bites on their lovers. Again, these bites have very romantic, evocative names like *bindu*, 'line of corals', 'jewel chain', 'broken cloud', etc., depending on whether they are single bites, or in a group or a line.

It shouldn't surprise us to learn that sadomasochism also finds a place in the *Kama Sutra*. He says some lovers derive great pleasure from 'striking' and 'thrashing'. But he also mentions that these actions should be completely mutual and only up to the point where they give pleasure. Should the woman at any point ask you to stop, you must respect her wishes. Nor should you use all these techniques at the same time. Novelty is great for kindling the flame of passion, but it is consideration and tenderness that keeps it alive for a long time to come.

She Loves Me, She Loves Me

The whole point of being in love and making love is mutual pleasure and satisfaction on many planes. During sex, it's the physical side that is important. So take some time to discover each other's preferences, erogenous zones and turn-offs. And don't forget your lessons.

Vatsyayana has said a woman takes longer to get aroused so foreplay is essential. Gauge her reactions to prolong foreplay or move on to penetration.

It is the sage's advice that when a man lies on his side he should have the woman on his left. But there is a proviso that says that in the case of an elephant-woman, the man should arouse her by stimulating her clitoris with his left hand.

A woman is aroused and satisfied by a man in two ways – externally and internally. After your kisses and embraces, slowly undress her. A shy girl will show inhibition which you should dispel by more kisses and caresses. When your penis is erect you should gently touch her all over her body and especially between her thighs. If it's her first time,

The knowledge of her erogenous zones and foreplay are essential for satisfying sex.

*Here's a tip: watch where she glances during lovemaking
and move to caress and fondle just those parts.*

touch her and stroke her especially on the breasts,
arms, shoulders, neck and thighs through her
clothes before persuading her to shed them. Twine
your fingers tightly in her hair when kissing her
on the mouth. Usually, a maiden closes her eyes
during her first union. But if she's already yours or
experienced you can proceed with any way pleasing
to both. The point is to learn all her erogenous
zones and caress her to heighten her desire till she

loses control. The fun part is that she's probably doing the same thing with you!

According to the *Kama Sutra*, the secret of satisfying her is to observe where she turns her glance during lovemaking and to continue caressing those parts with greater intensity. There are ten varieties of strokes and thrusts in coitus. Each has a name to go with the action:

❊ When you move in mildly and naturally it is called 'moving forward'.

❊ When you hold your penis in your hand and move it around inside her vagina it is 'churning'.

❊ When her vagina is on a lower level and you move in from on top, it is called 'piercing'.

❊ When she is on a higher level and you thrust from below and with some force, it is 'rubbing'.

❊ When you thrust in your penis with force and continue to do so, it is called 'pressing'.

❊ When the penis is partly withdrawn and then thrust back in, it's called 'giving a blow'.

❊ When you rub only one side of her vagina with your penis it's called 'the biting of a boar'.

❊ When both sides of her vagina are so rubbed it is the 'blow of a bull'.

❊ When you move without pausing between strokes it is called the 'sporting of a sparrow'. This usually happens when you're about to climax.

❊ When after ejaculating you do not withdraw but continue to lie with your penis inside her and your legs and hers are both stretched straight out and touching from thigh downwards it is called the 'perfect ending'. This can be done in any of three positions – when you're on top, when she's on top or if you are lying facing each other.

*After Cupid has shot his arrows, get ready to invite passion
into your life, learn the art of gentling into sex.*

The sudden relaxation of her body and the closing of her eyes indicate the onset of orgasm. Uncontrolled movements and the thrusting of her pelvis against yours accompany her climax. Learn to recognise these signs (very often one movement blends into the other) so that you can respond likewise.

When she shakes her hands, perspires, bites you, prevents you from getting up, kicks her legs and continues to move even after you have finished you'll know that her desires have not been completely satisfied. In that case, it is recommended that you extend foreplay and stimulate her clitoris for a longer time before penetrating her the next time.

Vatsyayana advises a certain degree of style and elegance to the entire act of making love. He says that before sex you should welcome your lover with good food, wine, music and entertaining conversation. Caress her gently. And only then when all her senses are heightened to a certain level should you get down to the actual physical act. Just as there is a heightening of all the senses before making love, so too there should be a cooling off period when both are sated. You should each take time off to have separate washes or take separate showers and then meet again to sit down in a cool place, eat or drink something pure, cool and soothing, perhaps cuddle each other if you wish and converse as old, affectionate friends.

The Many Ways of Love

Lovers who spend time with each other in pleasant ways both before and after sex create a certain level of confidence in each other. This heightens the love and of course the lovemaking because it makes you more sensitive to each other.

The sages have described love as being of four different kinds:

❊ Love resulting from the constant and habitual performance of some act is called the love born of continual habit. This would include love of sexual intercourse, love of sport, gambling, drinking and so on.

❊ Love which is felt for some novelty like oral sex, for instance, or love that arises from some anticipated pleasure is called love arising from the imagination.

❊ Love which is mutual and equally reciprocated and proves to be true on both sides and in which each lover looks upon the other as his or her very own is called the love resulting from belief.

Love, that plumbless theme, was divided by the sages into four kinds. Each, they exhorted, was to be enjoyed sensitively.

❋ Moreover, the perception and enjoyment of external objects results in the kind of loving pleasure which is recognised and appreciated by everybody. This is known as the type of love resulting or coming from the perception of

∾

You can be a naughty boy but inform your actions with the understanding that a man and a woman are meant to be a pair not selfish desire-seekers.

external objects and it embraces the other three kinds of love too.

Vatsyayana describes some more forms of love that bring about different types of sexual union.

When a man and woman who have been in love with each other for a long time come together after great difficulty or after a long separation or following a lovers' quarrel it is called a 'loving union'. This union can carry on for as long as they want and in any way that they mutually desire.

When lovers unite while their love is young and just flowering it is called the 'union of subsequent love'.

When you need to stimulate yourself artificially or when you have sex with a woman even though both of you actually love other people, it is called the 'union of artificial love'. In this case both of you need to use certain arousal techniques described in the *Kama Sutra*.

When you're engaged in sex with a woman but all through the act are thinking of someone else whom you love, you are taking part in a 'union of transferred love'.

If you indulge in sex with an unfortunate or less-privileged woman just to satisfy your own desires it is called the 'union similar to that of eunuchs'. In this instance you should not use any loving embraces, kisses or arousal techniques.

When a woman does the same thing it is known as a 'degrading or deceitful union' and the same strictures apply to her.

When two people who know and love each other deeply unite then the arousal technique is called the 'spontaneous union'. This is the most beautiful type of union and all the lovemaking techniques can be used freely.

Over the ages, a great deal has been written about the traditional positions used by men and women during sex. Most people seem to assume that the man goes on top because his is the more active and dominant role. While this is generally true, Indian sages have also recorded that reversing the position with the woman getting on top is a fantastic experience and one of the 'playful' aspects of sex. In this case, the woman makes all the movements and thrusts that you normally would.

⌇

Sometimes no one needs to be on top; otherwise, role reversal can work wonders for your sex life.

When she's exhausted, but neither of you has climaxed, turn around without withdrawing from her and begin all over again. With a little bit of practice and control you can carry on this 'roll over' game for quite some time! However, Vatsyayana sounds a note of warning here. The sage says that women who are excessively small or very large built, women who have their periods or those who have recently had a baby should not be allowed to take the top position as it is dangerous to their health.

While on the playful aspect of sex, we need to look at the matter of oral sex too. Let us note that this is the only time when Vatsyayana becomes a little censorious. He describes and comments on oral sex as a sport indulged in by eunuchs, servants of rich men and debauched women. In other words, people who have no say in the way they want to have sex. According to Vatsyayana, all religious texts forbid the act as it is viewed as an unclean act. This, however, doesn't prevent the sage from his scientific description of the various ways in which the penis is taken into the mouth and stimulated.

He mentions that oral sex can take place between the man and woman lying inversely and facing each other's genitalia, or between women who have the desire but limited access to men or between two men as the case may be. He also says that in some cases, on some occasions and in some places certain persons may find oral sex useful or satisfying. Therefore each person must consider all the social, physical and moral aspects and act accordingly.

She Loves Me Not

*T*his is the difficult part. What do you do when the two of you quarrel? How do you know when one's in the offing? And how do you handle it? Don't worry: the *Kama Sutra* also tells you how to deal with lovers' quarrels.

First of all you need to be sensitive to her feelings. When she is very much in love with you and both of you are relaxed after a great time in bed, it would be exceedingly callous of you to mention your ex-girlfriends. This will only serve to upset and aggravate her. She will throw a tantrum and get both physically and verbally abusive.

How do you pacify her? Pick her up tenderly and put her back on the bed, stroke her. Vatsyayana says now her rage will increase and she'll probably lash out or hurt herself. Finally, she'll get up and rush to the door. But in all probability won't leave. It's up to you now to say how sorry you are and coax her back with sweet words. If she does leave and goes away to a friend's house, you should send feelers through a trusted friend. Of

Ceaselessly admire her beauty of form, love her with words, coax her back into your arms after a quarrel.

*Absentmindedness followed by open contempt are
clear signs that she has lost interest.*

course, she reacts so violently as she's deeply in love with you. If her love were not so intense, her reaction wouldn't be so strong either. And as she truly loves you, your chances of being forgiven are very good.

Sometimes, it happens that your lover falls in love with someone else. Instead of being the proverbial last one to know, you should be alert to subtle behaviour changes and body language and prepare yourself for what's coming.

The first sign that something is wrong is when she appears to be absentminded. The next sign is when she openly dismisses what you say or do, makes fun of you in private and public and makes her contempt evident. Then she denies you sexual favours. The last stage is when she walks out on you or throws you out.

Again, it may be you who are tired of her. Here too, your behaviour will convey your meaning. You should pretend disinterest in her. Make promises you'll never keep. Underperform in bed or don't touch her at all. Speak with your friends and others in a mysterious fashion. If none of this seems to work, spend your nights elsewhere.

However, only a tiny part of the *Kama Sutra* is devoted to lovers' quarrels and what to do about them and that too as a sort of contingency plan. The entire purpose of the treatise is to bring loving couples together and help them stay together.

Forever Mine

The ultimate commitment to staying together is marriage. The society of Vatsyayana's times believed marriage was not to be either undertaken or dismissed lightly. Vatsyayana says when you marry a pure girl of the same caste according to your religion and society, the results of the union can only be positive.

Look for a bride from among your own people and class because a union where you share values, beliefs and living standards on an equal platform is best.

Your wife should come from a well-placed family. Both her parents should be living and she should be at least three years younger than you. She should have beauty and character and health. It is vital for the man to possess all these qualities too.

When your family and friends approve of your selection they should support you in every way. Her mother especially needs to be convinced you are the most suitable candidate. The sage concludes that marriage with a woman who at first sight

Choose a bride compatible in all respects, develop trust, respect and love – they will see you home.

pleases the mind and delights the eye always results in a harmonious union.

The marriage ceremony needs to be performed keeping all religious and social requirements in mind. The bridegroom should woo his bride gradually to gain her confidence, starting gently when it comes to sex. For couples who do not know each other at all, Vatsyayana advises celibacy for the first ten nights.

Vatsyayana's advice on the practical side of life after marriage may seem old-fashioned. We should remember that then child-brides were the norm. Today, the advice is good for a woman just getting to know you.

The most important concept he puts across is that you must be gentle and considerate with your wife. The second consideration is that it makes for a far more stable marriage if both of you get to know each other's minds and hearts before committing your bodies. (Today, a strong school of thought feels physical compatibility is *the* vital part of living together.) The third aspect of marriage is that both partners need to adjust to each other. This happens gradually with a great deal of mutual love and understanding. Vatsyayana's last and most important conclusion is that a successful relationship *has* to be based on trust, respect and love in equal measures.

Of all human interactions, the man-woman relationship is one of the oldest, one of the most enduring and paradoxically one of the frailest that we know. The *Kama Sutra* gives us an amazing insight into the feeling we call love and gives us also the means to nourish and sustain it till perpetuity.